Manchester University Mark I computer, 1949. On 21st June 1948 the prototype of this machine became the first computer to run a stored program.

CALCULATING MACHINES AND COMPUTERS

Geoffrey Tweedale

Shire Publications Ltd

CONTENTS

Printed in Great Britain by C. I. Thomas & Sons (Haverfordwest) Ltd, Press Buildings, Merlins Bridge, Haverfordwest, Dyfed SA61 1XF.

British Library Cataloguing in Publication Data: Tweedale, Geoffrey. Calculating machines and computers. 1. Computers, history I. Title. 621.3909. ISBN 0-7478-0080-4.

ACKNOWLEDGEMENTS
I am grateful to the following individuals and firms for information and help with the photographs: Apple Computers Incorporated: Dr Jim Bennett of the Whipple Museum, Cambridge; Dr Martin Campbell-Kelly; Gordon Collinson of the ICL Historical Collection; Dr David Edgerton; IBM UK Ltd; Mike Koiston; Sir Clive Sinclair; James Small; Don Manning; University of Cambridge Computer Laboratory; and Professor Konrad Zuse. Illustrations are acknowledged as follows: Apple Computers Incorporated, page 30 (bottom); Cray Research Incorporated, page 31; Electronic Research Associates Incorporated, page 26 (bottom); Ferranti, page 24 (bottom); IBM, pages 3, 4 (top), 5 (bottom), 6 (top and centre), 7, 8, 9 (top and bottom), 10, 11, 12 (bottom), 13, 14 (top), 15, 16, 18 (bottom right), 20 (bottom), 22, 23, 27 (bottom), 28, 29 (bottom); ICL, pages 18 (top and bottom left) and 30 (top); Illustrated London News, page 14 (bottom); National Archive for the History of Computing, pages 1 and 27 (top); Public Records Office, page 24 (top); Sir Clive Sinclair, page 29 (top); University of Cambridge Computer Laboratory, pages 25 (top) and 26 (top); Whipple Museum, cover and page 2; after M. R. Williams, page 9 (centre); Professor Konrad Zuse, page 21.

Cover picture shows (left to right) Napier's 'bones' and a seventeenth-century manual for their use; an abacus; an electronic pocket calculator; (centre) a nineteenth-century engineer's ivory slide-rule.

Left: A selection of pocket calculators, including (bottom right) the Sinclair Executive (1972).

Original Odhner calculator, 1890, the forerunner of the popular Brunsviga models.

THE FIRST CALCULATORS

Most people are familiar with both the computer, with its screen, keyboard and disc drives, and with the pocket calculator, so convenient for laborious sums. They are also aware that there is a difference between these two devices, without always being able to define it.

Before the 1940s this distinction between calculating and computing did not exist. The word 'computing' then meant only one thing — a clerk equipped with a hand calculating machine, who could 'compute' the standard calculations for wages, actuarial tables and ballistics. Calculating this way had its disadvantages: for complex problems it was slow, and the mechanical devices then in use, though they had evolved over many centuries, were unable to store more than a few digits. In the 1940s, however, advances in mathematics and electronics allowed the construction of a machine with an internal store or memory. Henceforth, data and programs could be held in the machine and automatically altered during computation. Such machines were *universal*, capable of providing the solution to any mathematical problem once an appropriate program had been inserted. The electronic stored-program digital computer had arrived.

Thus the modern computer is the latest of a long line of mechanical aids to computation: it is distinguished from them not by a magical new method of reasoning or calculation, but by being automatic, general-purpose and high-speed. It is the comprehensiveness of their automatic control which is the essentially novel feature of computers and differentiates them from their mechanical ancestors, although this line has become blurred in recent years as advances in electronics enable us to carry calculators that are effectively pocket computers, with memory functions that would be the envy of post-war computer pioneers.

The first calculating machine was probably the abacus, invented in Babylonia (now Iraq). This device embodied a momentous idea — that a machine could be used to perform intellectual work. The abacus (from the Greek *abakos* or *abax*, meaning 'board' or 'tablet') was

The abacus was one of the earliest, and most effective, of the early calculating devices. In the hands of a skilled operator it was a powerful aid to computation.

widespread in Europe until the late nineteenth century and is still used in some countries, such as Russia. In its earliest form it was merely a row of shallow grooves and lines traced on the ground, with pebbles, stones or bones used as counters: the rows represented units, such as tens and hundreds, and the quantity of counters in the rows represented a number. The abacus rapidly became indispensable, mainly because of its simplicity of use in societies where number systems were complex and difficult to use for reckoning. This was the case with Roman numerals (try, for example, dividing MDCLIX by LIV in

your head). Gradually, by the end of the sixteenth century, the modern number system based on Hindu-Arabic mathematics had become widespread, leading to the demise of the abacus in the West, though not in the East, where, in the familiar form of the counting frame, it is still used. The Hindu-Arabic system greatly facilitated arithmetic and also paved the way for mechanical methods of calculation.

From the early seventeenth century onwards numerous philosophers and mathematicians devised increasingly sophisticated machines. Amongst them was John Napier (1550-1617), a wealthy

Figure 1 shows one basic abacus method. The number 254 has been registered. Other numbers can be added by pushing up more beads. In the second method (figure 2) 715 has been registered. Beads below xy in Section A count for one each and those above xy are worth five. This device was sometimes called the Heaven and Earth abacus.

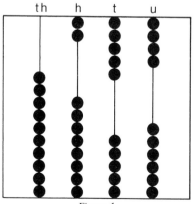

Figure 1

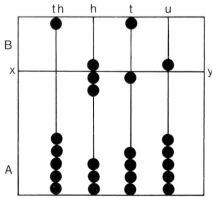

Figure 2

4

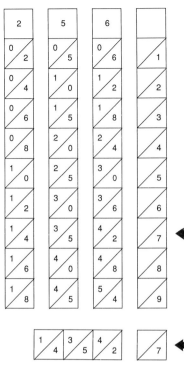

Answer

1   7   9   2

Above: *Napier's rods or 'bones'*
were a multiplication table in col-
umns. For example: to multiply
256 by 7, the 2, 5 and 6 rods were
selected, alongside the 1 rod. The 7
line was then read, adding the
numbers diagonally to produce the
answer — 1792. (See cover pic-
ture.)

laird from near Edinburgh, who, as well as having an interest in religious philosophy, was also a gifted mathematician. Napier is best known for the invention of logarithms or logs — a series of numbers that enables multiplication and division to be done by addition and subtraction. Instead of multiplying and dividing natural numbers (1, 2, 3, *et cetera*) on paper or in one's head, one simply looked them up in log tables and added or subtracted the given figures; the final answer was produced by converting the sum of the logs back to a natural number by referring to a table of antilogs. Napier made his logarithms known in 1614, though it took other mathematicians more than a decade to calculate and publish the tables of numbers. Henceforth, compiling specialised mathematical tables for engineers, navigators and scientists became a full-time occupation for generations of mathematicians.

Shortly before his death Napier also devised a gadget for multiplication. Using an ancient numerical scheme known as the Arabian lattice, he laid out a special version of the multiplication tables on a set of square wooden rods: there was a rod, or numbered stick, for each of the ten digits including zero. Napier's rods or 'bones' were essentially a multiplication table in columns. Enormously popular throughout Europe,

Right: *John Napier's early 'pocket*
calculator' designed in about 1617.

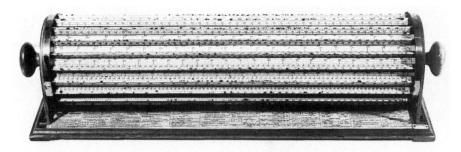

Above: *The slide-rule, an analogue device, reached a high degree of sophistication. In 1881 E. Thacher, a New York inventor, patented this huge cylindrical rule. By using a compass, computations could be performed that were accurate to four places.*

Left: *Wilhelm Schickard's Calculating Clock (1623) was the first mechanical calculator. Its main sections were an arithmetical unit in the middle (for simple multiplications) and six cycle counters beneath for addition and subtraction.*

Right: *The six numbered dials on the lower part of Schickard's Calculating Clock were connected to six axles in the box beneath. The chief technical problem was how to carry from one set of digits to the next. Schickard cleverly solved this by using a single-toothed 'mutilated' gear, which on every complete turn would engage an intermediate wheel and advance the next counter by one.*

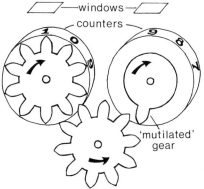

Napier's invention was often sold in portable *de luxe* cases.

By the 1650s the slide-rule had appeared, the work of two Englishmen, Edmund Gunter (1581-1626) and the Reverend William Oughtred (1574?-

Eight-digit Pascaline (c.1642). Expensive, mechanically unreliable and mathematically limited (it was mostly useful only for basic addition), Pascal's calculator nevertheless was a historic achievement: it demonstrated that a machine could be used for the intellectual task of counting.

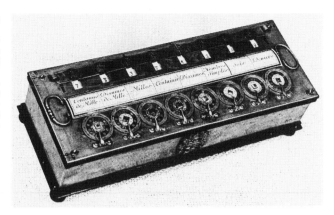

1660). Gunter developed a ruler (Gunter's scale), 2 feet (60 cm) in length, marked proportionally with Napier's logarithms. Multiplication and division were done by marking off lengths along the rule with dividers. Oughtred eliminated the need for dividers by sliding another ruler alongside the first and thus developed the familiar slide-rule with a rigid frame and a sliding central ruler.

The slide-rule is regarded as the first analogue computer, in which multiplication is carried out by the addition of lengths. (The difference between *analogue* and *digital* devices is an important one in the history of computing. Most calculators and computers are digital devices, counting numbers in the standard way. But an historically important class of scientific instruments and computers — scales, slide rules, thermometers, and clocks with hands — are analogue devices, in which measurements are made by analogy between two quantities.)

The first mechanical calculator was invented by Wilhelm Schickard (1592-1635), a German scholar who was professor of Hebrew and oriental languages at Tübingen University. In 1623 Schickard built a Calculating Clock, as he called it, and wrote to Johannes Kepler, the great mathematician and astronomer, describing it. But these details were lost until they were discovered by chance amongst the correspondence of the two men in the 1950s. This allowed the machine to be reconstructed. It consisted of two devices in one: the top was

simply a version of Napier's bones laid out on six cylinders in a box, with wooden slats. For bigger calculations, Schickard installed a mechanical adder beneath.

Schickard's device was forgotten, so that the Frenchman Blaise Pascal (1623-62) has usually been regarded as the inventor of the mechanical calculator. A child prodigy, Pascal's accomplishments spanned mathematics, physics and philosophy, before he retired prematurely to a life of religious contemplation. He began work on his calculator in 1642 when he was nineteen, spurred by the problems his father faced as a tax collector in Rouen. The result of his labours was the Pascaline, a multi-digit calculator about the size of a shoe box, 1 foot (30 cm) long, with dials at the front for entering the numbers and crown-type gears on the inside for calculating the answers, which appeared in little windows on the face. It worked well for basic addition, less efficiently for subtraction, and laboriously for multiplication and division. Though it made Pascal famous, it proved mechanically unreliable, and perhaps only a dozen were sold.

The need for mechanical aids to calculation was felt in other countries. In Britain Sir Samuel Morland (1625-95), Master of Mechanics to King Charles II, built two calculating machines in the 1660s. In France René Grillet, a clockmaker to Louis XIV, built an arithmetic machine in 1678 that was influenced by the work of Pascal. These devices worked with varying degrees of success but lacked reliability.

The third great calculator inventor of the seventeenth century was Gottfried von Leibniz (1646-1716). Famous for his invention of calculus and pioneering work on the algebraic system of numbering, on which modern computers are based, Leibniz's logical and wide-ranging mind led him to construct a machine in which addition and multiplication could be performed 'with greatest speed and accuracy'. The calculator, or Stepped Reckoner as he called it, was built in the early 1670s. An important feature was the Leibniz wheel, a special gear which acted as a mechanical multiplier. Capable of four arithmetic operations, it was more sophisticated than either the Calculating Clock or the Pascaline, but apparently Leibniz never perfected it. The only surviving version, in a museum in Hanover, Germany, is an inoperative relic.

Nevertheless, the Stepped Reckoner

Right: *Samuel Morland's adding machine, 1666, which the inventor described as a 'new and useful instrument for addition and subtraction of pounds, shillings, pence and farthings'.*

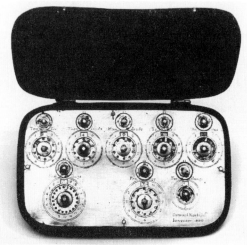

Left: *Calculating machines designed by René Grillet, 1678. Although unsophisticated — the lower section was simply a set of Napier's 'bones' on cylinders — Grillet's machine would have been useful in a society where only pen and ink were available for recording intermediate results.*

Above: *A replica of Leibniz's calculating machine. Known as the Stepped Reckoner, its operating principles paved the way for the first successful commercially produced mechanical calculators.*

Right: *This simplified diagram shows the nine graduated teeth that were at the heart of Leibniz's Stepped Reckoner. In order to add, say, five to the number on the answer dial at the right, it was only necessary to move the pointer to the appropriate place and turn the drum once. The gear meshed with the drum teeth and the dial was turned five digits. Leibniz's device had eight of these mechanisms, all turned by a single crank. Multiplication was performed by repeatedly turning the drum.*

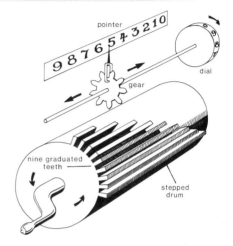

was an important invention, which inspired many imitators and eventually led to the development of the first mechanical calculators. In 1775-7, for example, the third Earl Stanhope (1753-1816) built two successful devices based on the Leibniz wheel, but more rugged and reliable. However, the production of such machines for the commercial market was still more than fifty years away, because of mechanical and engineering problems and complexities in their use, as well as the small number of customers.

Calculating engine designed by Charles, Viscount Mahon (later Earl Stanhope), c.1776. Based on Leibniz's stepped-gear principle (though considerably more robust), this device could multiply or divide by the method of successive addition or subtraction and could deal with numbers up to twelve digits.

The Arithmometer (1820), the first successful calculating machine, multiplied and divided by repeated addition and subtraction. The multiplicand was set using the six indicators, numbered 0 to 9. These indicators slid a pinion with ten teeth along a square axle, beneath which was a stepped cylinder. The knob (left centre) set the machine either for addition or subtraction. For multiplication, the multiplicand was set and the crank at bottom right was turned the number of times indicated by the unit figure of the multiplier and the result was transferred to the registers located under the hinged top-plate of the machine. The plate was then raised and shifted one position to the left, after which the crank was turned the number of times indicated by the ten digits of the multiplier — and so on. For subtraction and division, the correct setting was made by moving the knob at left centre, causing the wheels underneath to rotate in the reverse direction.

NINETEENTH-CENTURY PIONEERS

Commercially successful calculators eventually appeared in the early nineteenth century. The Arithmometer, as he called it, was invented in 1820 by the Frenchman Charles Xavier Thomas de Colmar (1785-1870). He ran an insurance company in Paris, where the nature of the work led him to devise a calculating machine which could add, subtract, multiply and divide. A first-rate piece of practical engineering, the Arithmometer was compact, easy to use and based on the Leibniz wheel. It was the first commercially produced calculator and about 1500 models were sold within thirty years. Such devices were becoming a necessity in Britain and other parts of Europe in the early nineteenth century when the industrial revolution was in full swing. Scientists, businessmen and the government found themselves in an increasingly numerical world.

After 1875 developments in manufacturing technology and engineering led to rapid progress in mechanical calculators. Various inventors devised machines for arithmetic: for example, Frank Stephen Baldwin of St Louis; the Swedish engineer, Willgodt Theophil Odhner; Ramon Verea, a Spaniard living in New York; and the Frenchman Léon Bollée. But most of their machines, though they worked well, did not achieve extensive sales. They were useful in scientific calculations, but, being 'lever-set', were too slow for routine accounting. In 1885, however, Dorr E. Felt, who worked as a mechanic for the Pullman Company in

Above left: *Frank Stephen Baldwin's machine of 1875 replaced the Leibniz stepped wheel with a pin-wheel, so eliminating the reversing gears previously needed to switch from addition to subtraction. Operating the machine involved setting the levers on the slotted cylinder and turning the crank clockwise to add or multiply, anticlockwise to subtract or divide. Answers appeared in the long row of holes in the machine casing. The short row of holes beneath registered a multiplier or quotient.*

Above right: *In 1892 Otto Stigler obtained a German patent for a machine embodying Bollée's ideas and by the following year he had perfected a more compact device, called the Millionaire. A single turn of the operating crank not only produced one partial product in a multiplication but automatically added it to the previous result and reset the machine for the next operation. The Millionaire could perform all arithmetic calculations relatively speedily, which made it popular in laboratories and engineering shops.*

Below left: *Dorr E. Felt's prototype for the Comptometer. With a jack-knife as his principal tool, Felt assembled this model from a macaroni box, using meat skewers for keys and elastic bands for springs.*

Below right: *The Comptometer, the first successful key-driven multiple-order calculating machine, was patented by Felt in 1887. Commercial production began two years later, when this popular and fast calculator was advertised as 'the machine-gun of the office'.*

11

First in Use (1892)

First in Usefulness in Over 300 Different Lines of Business

First in the Hearts of Over 63,000 Users

The Burroughs
Adding and Listing Machine

Part of an advertisement for the Burroughs adding and listing machine which appeared in the February 1908 issue of the 'Office Appliances Magazine'.

Chicago, made the pivotal breakthrough with the invention of a 'key-set' calculator, which had a typewriter-style keyboard, allowing numbers to be entered quickly. From his crude prototype, he developed in 1886 the highly successful Comptometer adding machine. Another American inventor, William S. Burroughs (1857-98), added an important refinement to this idea in 1892 when he patented a keyboard (though not key-driven) adder-lister which produced a printed record of what had been entered, with the total at the end. This machine was to outsell every other calculator on the market.

At the same time that calculating machines for office use were being improved another generation of machines was developing in the nineteenth century. Accurate published numerical tables were increasingly required in engineering, science, mathematics and navigation. But even the most widely used books of tables contained mathematical or printing errors. In the early nineteenth century it occurred to an English mathematician, Charles Babbage (1792-1871), that the figures for tables might be calculated and printed by machine. Babbage, like many calculating-machine pioneers, had an extraordinarily wide range of interests, which

included mathematics, philosophy, engineering and economics. Born in London, he was educated at Cambridge University, where he eventually held the Lucasian chair of mathematics. While a student there, he was sitting in the rooms of the Analytical Society, an undergraduate mathematics club, when a member entered and called out: 'Well, Babbage, what are you dreaming about?' To which Babbage replied: 'I am thinking that all these Tables [pointing to the logarithms] might be calculated by machinery.' Thereafter Babbage spent most of his life (and a good deal of his money) in attempting to build machines to calculate mathematical tables automatically.

The first of his inventions, the Difference Engine, was intended for the calculation of tables by repeated addition performed by trains of gear wheels. A small prototype model was described to the Astronomical Society in 1822 and was awarded the Society's first gold medal. Babbage was then granted money by the government to build a full-sized machine. But in 1842, after some £17,000 of public money and £6,000 of his own had been spent trying to overcome various engineering problems and the complexities of the machine without any substantial result, government support was withdrawn. A prototype of the machine

is now in the Science Museum, London.

Meanwhile, Babbage had conceived a much more sophisticated device, the Analytical Engine, which was designed to perform many different computations. Information was to be inserted on punched cards, which were to store not only the numbers but also the sequence of operations to be performed. (The idea of using punched cards derived from the Jacquard mechanism for producing patterns on a loom.) It was an ambitious idea and, like the Difference Engine, it was never realised. Doubtless the mechanical technologies of the day would have permitted Babbage's designs to be completed only with great difficulty and cost; and his perfectionism also hindered the project. Nevertheless, Babbage's vision of a machine that was, in effect, a programmable calculator has been recognised as the germ of the modern computer.

Where Babbage failed, others succeeded. In the 1830s a Swedish lawyer, Pehr Georg Scheutz (1785-1873), who

Charles Babbage, the English mathematician and polymath, is sometimes referred to as the pioneer of the modern computer but his practical achievements and influence were limited.

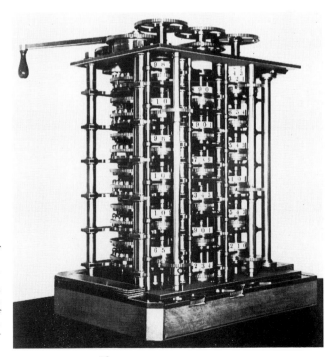

Babbage's prototype of the Difference Engine, built in 1822, and now in the Science Museum, London. Some 2 feet (60 cm) high, this machine was only a small part of the whole Difference Engine, which was never completed.

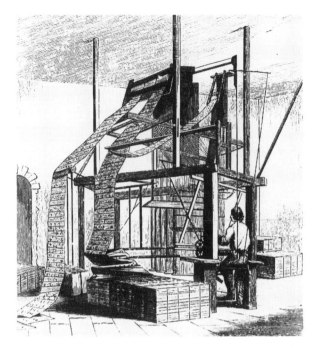

The programming of Babbage's Analytical Engine was based on punched cards, an idea first used in the textile industry by the Frenchman Joseph-Marie Jacquard to programme designs on looms weaving complex patterns. His automatic loom was controlled by a chain of rotating cards over a cylinder carrying the weft thread: as each card was presented to a mechanical reader, wooden needles either passed through the holes or were pressed in, allowing the warp thread to pass through or be blocked.

had read about Babbage's Difference Engine, began designing his own machine. The project was passed to his son Edvard Scheutz (1821-81), an engineer, who had been born in Stockholm and educated at the Royal Technological Institute. Edvard, with considerably less money than Babbage, constructed the

The world's first operable and useful Difference Engine was available in Sweden by 1854, the work of Georg and Edvard Scheutz.

world's first Difference Engine in 1843 and built a second version ten years later. It mechanised the production of numerical tables, but owing to the limited demand for such machines the Scheutzes were unable to market it profitably.

The idea of using punched cards was developed successfully, though with a less ambitious objective, by Herman Hollerith (1860-1929), an American inventor-entrepreneur, who set himself the

Above: *Herman Hollerith. As a special agent for the United States census, his inventive talents were brought to bear on mechanising the enumeration of the American population.*

task of mechanising the counting and analysis of the population of the United States in the national census of 1890.

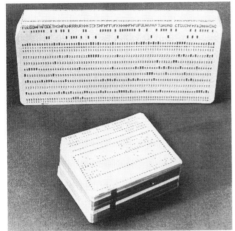

Above: *At the heart of Hollerith's invention, as with those of Jacquard and Babbage, was the use of punched cards to store data. In the 1890 census Hollerith's cards contained information on sex, race, birthplace, occupation and many other characteristics.*

Right: *A Hollerith machine operator at work in 1890, inserting a punched card into the reader.*

Hollerith had joined the Census Office in Washington, DC, as a special agent. Here he had become aware of a pressing problem: in 1880, although the head-count of the US population had taken only a few months, the laborious manual methods used for the analysis and tabulation of the data took years to complete. Hollerith had soon devised a solution based on punched cards (perhaps also learned from the Jacquard loom) to store data. He invented both a special puncher and a card reader. The positions of holes in the card indicated sex, nationality, age and so on. The card reader had a panel of counting dials. As the card was fed into the machine it was 'read' by an array of pins over cups of mercury. When the pins passed through the holes into the mercury this completed an electric circuit and advanced the appropriate dials on the machine. Using Hollerith's machines, some operators handled about seven thousand cards a day (the record was 19,071) and only six weeks after the count had begun the census had a tally: 62,622,250.

Hollerith's census machine was the first punched-card data processor. In 1896 he established his own company, the Tabulating Machine Company, and began supplying orders worldwide. Private industry and government in both America and Europe found Hollerith's machines indispensable. Though competition soon appeared from other American entrepreneurs, such as James Powers (1871-1915), by the early 1900s Hollerith's firm had more business than it could handle.

Hollerith's tabulator and sorter of 1890. After each card had been punched, it was 'read' by a clerk seated at the tabulator (left). The reader was a small press, which used an array of pins to locate the punched holes and produce an electrical contact. Each contact advanced the dials on the front of the tabulator. The sorter (right) was simply a box with several compartments: when a card with a certain set of characteristics was read, a lid on the sorter opened and the operator filed the card in the appropriate compartment.

Portability, durability and relatively low price made the German Brunsviga one of the most popular calculating machines in Europe in the early twentieth century. The earliest Brunsviga designs were based on the work of the Swedish engineer E. T. Odhner, who invented a machine of the pin-wheel and cam-disk type.

THE EARLY TWENTIETH CENTURY

By the early twentieth century mechanical calculators were well established in the scientific laboratory and the office. The most common were the mechanical and electro-mechanical hand calculators which would add, subtract, multiply and divide two numbers. The major advances in these machines had been made in Germany, Sweden and the United States.

Many applications were found also for electro-mechanical punched-card machines, such as sorters and tabulators, derived from the pioneering work of Herman Hollerith and James Powers. Some of today's most important computer companies had their origins in supplying the demand for such machines. Chief among these was International Business Machines (IBM), which was established in 1911 in a merger of American companies (including Hollerith's) producing computing scales, time-recording and tabulating machines. IBM became prominent in the 1920s, under the leadership of Thomas J. Watson (1874-1956), who cleverly exploited the market for tabulators. When American industry boomed in the 1920s IBM benefited from private-sector expansion; when it slumped in the Depression of the 1930s, the firm still had plenty of orders from the public sector. American commercial rivalry was transferred across the Atlantic when in 1907 a British-owned subsidiary of the Hollerith company, the British Tabulating Machine Company Limited, was formed, to be followed eight years later by a subsidiary of the Powers company, the Accounting and Tabulating Corporation of Great Britain. These two firms also flourished in the 1920s and were the progenitors of Britain's largest indigenous information-systems company, ICL.

Although punched-card machinery could be adapted for scientific work, generally such calculators were not very good at solving highly complex mathematical problems. Hence during the inter-war period a number of machines that tried a different approach were constructed.

Right: *This Hollerith tabulator was produced by the British Tabulating Machine Company in about 1924. Such machines were becoming a familiar sight in major offices at this time.*

Below: *Then, as now, the main advantage of calculating machines was that they saved time. The point is humorously made by the cartoonist Henry Bateman in this British Tabulating Machine Company advertisement.*

Amongst the most important mathematical formulations in science and engineering are differential equations. These equations, which are useful in ballistics and tidal and astronomical calculations, enable the prediction of the behaviour of moving objects according to certain variables. They are very difficult to solve. But Lord Kelvin (1824-1907), in a remarkable paper published in 1876, argued that a mechanical 'differential analyser' capable of solving these equations

Below: *An IBM logo of 1924.*

Vannevar Bush at the Massachusetts Institute of Technology watching the operation of the differential analyser, a machine he had built for intricate mathematical problems.

was theoretically possible. His brother, Professor James Thomson, had first thought of the idea. Basically, the machine used an 'integrator' (a wheel and disc arrangement with attached drive shafts) to effect the mathematical process of integration. But Victorian technology was incapable of realising Kelvin's ideas and so the machine was never built (though Kelvin did build a tide predictor in 1873). In about 1930, however, Van-nevar Bush (1890-1974), a professor of engineering at the Massachusetts Institute of Technology, returned to the problem and constructed a working differential analyser. Bush overcame the technical problems that had defeated Kelvin. In particular, he was able to incorporate into his machine a 'torque amplifier', which 'stepped up' the smallest forces of the numerous shafts and gears. The differential analyser — an

Professor Douglas R. Hartree (left) and his assistant, Arthur Porter, stand behind their prototype differential analyser at Manchester University in 1935. The machine was made from Meccano parts!

Punched-card equipment in use in the 1930s. Large offices were becoming increasingly dependent on such machines.

Howard Aiken's Mark I, completed in 1943, was an impressive sight. According to one physicist, when it was working it sounded 'like a roomful of ladies knitting'.

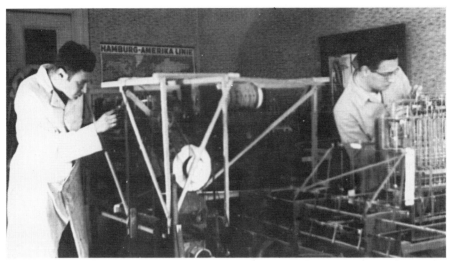

Konrad Zuse (right) and his collaborator, Helmut Schreyer, at work in Zuse's parents' living room in Berlin in about 1937.

analogue computer — demonstrated the potential of mechanisation for scientific applications and it influenced a generation of mathematicians and computer pioneers. An influential copy of Bush's analyser was built at Manchester University by Douglas R. Hartree (1897-1958) in 1935.

Important developments were also occurring in Germany, as a result of the work of Konrad Zuse. Born in Berlin, Zuse was educated at the Berlin Institute of Technology before joining the Henschel Aircraft Company in 1935. Here he was set to work on laborious linear equations, which spurred him to build a calculating machine in his spare time. His first machine, begun in 1936, and his subsequent ones were built in difficult circumstances. Zuse spent his own money and at first had to use the living room of his parents' apartment. He completed a number of prototypes, the most significant of which was the Z3, a small machine consisting of a tape reader, an operator's console and two cabinets for the 2600 relays. The Z3 had no internally stored program, but it was nevertheless the world's first machine that could be described as a fully working computer with automatic control (via punched tape) of its operations.

A more ambitious calculator project began in 1939 at Harvard University, where Howard H. Aiken (1900-73), a professor of mathematics, succeeded in gaining the support of IBM for the construction of an electro-mechanical calculator. As a mathematician Aiken had faced smilar problems to Zuse and wished to remove the labour from complex equations. He was also aware of Charles Babbage's work and became inspired by his example. Aiken's machine — the Automatic Sequence Controlled Calculator (ASCC), or Harvard Mark I — was built at an IBM plant in New York at a cost of $500,000. Completed by 1943, it was 8 feet (2.44 metres) tall, 51 feet (15.54 metres) long, 2 feet (60 cm) thick and weighed 5 tons, with about 750,000 parts. The Americans, unaware of Zuse, regarded it as a great achievement — the first program-controlled calculator. The program was held on a punched paper tape. The machine could multiply two 23 digit decimal numbers in three seconds and produce the answer on punched cards. However, the Mark I was obsolescent almost immediately: Aiken's giant mechanical calculator was about to be overtaken by stored-program digital computers.

Corporal Herman Goldstine (US Army liaison officer) and J. Presper Eckert holding a plug-in board for the ENIAC.

THE ELECTRONIC DIGITAL COMPUTER

After the Second World War there was a major advance in computing. Until 1945 data and instructions for various computing and calculating devices had always been stored *outside* the machine. This seemed logical: machinery had always been controlled from the outside — a worker keyed in the necessary data, a few controls were manipulated, and up came the answer. Now a new idea was to emerge — the stored-program concept — in which programs and data could be held *inside* the machine, making it immensely more powerful and faster.

Military need provided the context and spur for this innovation. In both Britain and the United States the demand for machines and scientists to perform the calculations for weaponry and code-breaking increased enormously. In America the world's first working electronic digital calculator had been built in the early 1940s by J. V. Atanasoff, a professor at Iowa State University, and one of his graduate students, Clifford Berry. This machine influenced the design of a major project at the Moore School of Electrical Engineering at the University of Pennsylvania, in Philadelphia. This resulted in the ENIAC (Electronic Numerical Integrator and Computer), which was built by a design team led by J. Presper Eckert and John Mauchly (1907-80). The ENIAC, which was built to calculate ballistics tables and became operational at the end of the war, contained 18,000 vacuum tubes and weighed 30 tons. This giant 'brain' gave the public its first dramatic glimpse of the coming computer age.

Meanwhile, a beleaguered Britain had directed its mathematical and engineering skills towards the construction of the 'Colossus', a code-breaking device which cleverly deciphered top-secret German messages and so helped win the war. Amongst the code-breakers was the mathematician Dr Alan Turing (1912-54), who in a pre-war mathematical publication had described a *hypothetical* machine with a scanner and a tape, which in principle possessed the characteristics of a stored-program computer. (After the war Turing actually built a computer at the National Physical Laboratory.) The skills developed at Bletchley Park, Buckinghamshire, where the Colossus was built in the utmost secrecy, provided a seedbed for later British developments.

However, neither the ENIAC nor the Colossus had an internal memory, though it was becoming apparent that such a feature would be desirable. A high-speed calculator, like the ENIAC for example, operated at the unprecedented pace of five thousand additions a second, making it impossible to feed in data and instructions fast enough.

Such a machine cried out for a memory. But the practical and theoretical problems of building such a machine were immense, especially since in 1945 no one had constructed an electronic memory or even knew whether it was feasible.

The theoretical ideas were solved by the American mathematician John Von Neumann (1903-57) and the Moore School engineers, who were then planning another machine, the EDVAC (Electronic Discrete Variable Computer). In 1945 Von Neumann wrote a 'First Draft of a Report on the EDVAC', which was widely circulated. Although Von Neumann's ideas depended on the contribution of his co-workers (which he did not acknowledge), he was the first to describe in detail the concept of the stored-program digital computer — a machine based on a central control unit that would orchestrate all operations, with a central processor and a random-access read/write memory. Von Neumann's world-wide fame as a mathematical genius guaranteed that computers would now be taken seriously and his report had an immense influence. (Com-

A dramatic view of the ENIAC at the Moore School in Philadelphia in 1946. Herman Goldstine is entering a number on one of the machine's three function tables.

The Colossus, the British government's code-breaking machine at Bletchley Park. The paper-tape was read by photo-electric cells.

puters based on this concept are sometimes known as 'Von Neumann machines'.)

The construction of a memory and the actual building of such a machine was, however, first achieved in England. In 1946 Professor Sir F. C. Williams (1911-77) and Professor Tom Kilburn began work at Manchester University with the intention of developing a novel form of computer storage using cathode ray tubes. The storage system built around these tubes (which were soon aptly named Williams tubes) was perfected in the following year and a small prototype

machine was built. On 21st June 1948 the Manchester machine became the world's first electronic digital stored-program computer to execute a program. Later the Williams-Kilburn team collaborated with the local electronics firm, Ferranti Limited, to produce a commercial version of the machine, the Ferranti Mark I.

Meanwhile, at Cambridge University Professor Maurice V. Wilkes headed a team which in 1949 built the EDSAC (Electronic Delay Storage Automatic Calculator), an influential computer around which Wilkes and his colleagues developed a proper computing service —

A view of the Ferranti Mark I, with Dr Alan Turing standing to the right of the operator's console. Derived from its Manchester University namesake, the Ferranti Mark I was arguably the world's first commercial stored-program computer when it was delivered in February 1951.

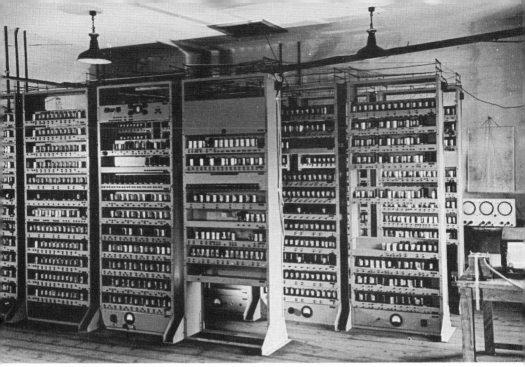

The Cambridge University EDSAC. Although this stored-program computer was a copy of the American EDVAC design, it was nevertheless operational before its counterpart.

The LEO computer, 1953. Built by the catering firm Lyons with the assistance of the Cambridge University EDSAC team and other electronics firms, this computer pioneered in Britain the use of electronic digital computers in business.

the first in the world — with a library of suitable programs. The Cambridge team also collaborated with the catering firm J. Lyons and Company in constructing the LEO (Lyons Electronic Office). This machine pioneered in Britain the use of computers for business data-processing. It also launched Lyons into the computer business, since about a hundred LEO machines were eventually built.

In the United States, where the implementation of ideas had been delayed by the fragmentation of research teams after the war and the lack of a suitable storage device, the ENIAC had provided the basis for a proliferation of stored-program computers in the early 1950s. Eckert and Mauchly developed the Univac I, delivered in 1951 to the US Bureau of Census, which was the first computer to use magnetic tape to store data and the first commercially produced American computer.

Of major importance for the development of American and British computers in the 1950s was the support of government, which needed the machines for military applications. The IBM Stretch and the Univac LARC machines, introduced in about 1960, were examples of high-speed computer projects funded by the military. The Manchester Atlas computer, which on its introduction in 1963 was regarded as the fastest computer in

The EDSAC team in 1947. The project leader, Maurice Wilkes, is the bespectacled figure in the foreground.

the world, was also mainly used by scientific and military establishments.

The momentum generated by these efforts soon spilled over into the business world. For a while the punched-card office machines and analogue computers held their share of the market, but in the mid 1960s demand collapsed as stored-program computers made their presence felt. IBM, which had benefited greatly

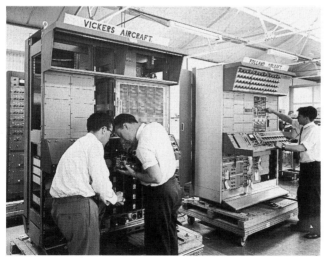

Despite the spread of electronic digital computers in the 1950s and 1960s, analogue devices continued to be important in specialist applications, such as aircraft design.

from United States government support, was well placed to exploit the business market, too. In 1964, only ten years after it had introduced its first commercial electronic stored-program computer (the 701), IBM launched the System/360, a comprehensive family of compatible computers, which reshaped the entire computer industry. For the first time the IBM System/360 offered potential purchasers an array of compatible processors and software packages that would suit almost any application or budget and could be upgraded without having to buy new peripherals and software. The huge success of this strategy secured IBM's position as the world's leading computer manufacturer.

The rapid development of the computer in the post-war era depended upon the gathering pace of electronics, which within a few decades had produced three

The IBM System/360 was introduced in April 1964. The System eventually included nine processors and over seventy peripherals and was the first 'family' of computers.

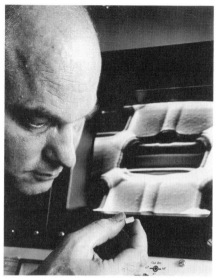

main 'generations'. The first, from 1940 to 1955, was based on electronic tube (valve) technology and punched card and paper tape for input/output. In the second, from 1955 to about 1960, transistors were introduced, with magnetic-core main memory and a wider range of input/output facilities (such as magnetic drums and early magnetic disks). With the third generation, from about 1960 to the present day, the integrated circuit (IC), in which computer components were fabricated on a single silicon chip, was introduced. This has led to computer components disappearing from sight as ingenious ways were found of packing a whole computer on to a chip no bigger than a thumbnail.

More sophisticated programs (software) for the computer were essential too. Programming an early computer was a difficult operation, often using a com-

Above: Miniaturisation underpinned advances in computing. This IBM engineer holds a computer memory chip that can store more than one million bits of information in a sliver of silicon only 7/32 inch (5.5 mm) by 3/8 inch (9.5 mm). Behind the chip is an image of a single one of its storage cells, magnified twenty thousand times.

Below: A technician inspects a polished 5 inch (127 mm) silicon wafer. Each wafer can contain five hundred chips and as many as 750,000 logic circuits.

Sir Clive Sinclair cleverly exploited the demand for pocket calculators and home computers.

plex machine code of binary numbers. As computer technology developed, however, high-level programming languages such as FORTRAN (FORmula TRANslation) were developed that used ordinary English phrases and mathematical expressions. Eventually a range of computer languages appeared that ensured that programming was no longer the domain of the specialist: these included COBOL (COmmon Business-Oriented Language), ALGOL (ALGOrithmic Language), and one of the most popular of all, BASIC (Beginner's All-purpose Symbolic Instruction Code).

Miniaturisation rejuvenated the calculator. In 1972 Sir Clive Sinclair introduced the Sinclair Executive calculator, the world's first pocket calculator. It was an enormous success and stimulated the production of countless pocket calculators of increasing sophistication. More importantly, the development of the silicon chip led to the ultimate in the popularisation of computing technology — the personal computer. A Massachusetts-based firm, Digital Equipment Corporation (DEC), indicated the future trend when in 1963 it introduced the PDP-8, the first successful minicomputer (about the size of a refrigerator). In 1975 a company in New Mexico, Micro Instrumentation and Telemetry Systems (MITS), marketed the Altair 8800 computer in both assembled and kit form. The Altair inspired many American hobbyists to design their own machines, amongst them

two young West Coast computer enthusiasts, Stephen Wozniak and Steven Jobs. They set up a partnership, the Apple Computer Company, and in 1977 introduced the Apple II, a machine that became the archetype of personal computers. Its success enabled Apple to become the fastest growing company in history. Not to be outdone, in 1981 IBM marketed its own personal computer, the PC. By 1983 sales of this machine were

The visual display unit (VDU), central processor, keyboard and printer of the personal computer — an increasingly familiar sight in the office and home.

29

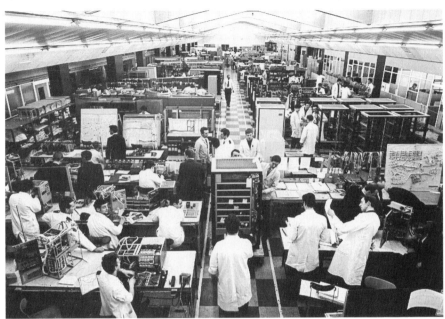

Computer production, old and new. In the 1960s computers, such as these under construction at the English Electric factory, were made in limited numbers and available only at a high price. By the 1990s computers had become a mass-produced commodity, rolling off the production line in their thousands, like these Apple Macintoshes.

A cutaway view of the Cray-1/S supercomputer, marketed in 1979 by Cray Research Incorporated, Minneapolis. Such high-speed scientific computers are used, for example, for complex calculations in weather forecasting and aerospace.

800,000 and the IBM PC became the most popular and influential personal computer. As the demand for these machines grew, other firms introduced low-priced IBM-compatible machines or secured a market-share with IBM PC-compatible software and peripherals.

Advances in computer technology show no sign of slackening. In the 1980s so-called 'supercomputers', such as the American Cray machines, capable of processing billions of instructions per second, have been constructed. The development of new computer chips, such as the Inmos transputer, which can process information in parallel rather than serially, offers further dramatic advances in speed. Some regard these breakthroughs as leading to the realisation of an old idea, a mechanical 'brain', using 'artificial intelligence'. Meanwhile, what was once an exotic and expensive technical tool has become an everyday commodity and an inescapable fact of twentieth-century life.

FURTHER READING

Augarten, Stan. *Bit by Bit: An Illustrated History of Computers*. Ticknor and Fields, New York, 1984.

Austrian, Geoffrey, D. *Herman Hollerith: Forgotten Giant of Information Processing*. Columbia University Press, New York, 1982.

Baxandall, D. (compiler). *Calculating Machines and Instruments*. Science Museum, revised edition (by Jane Pugh), 1975.

Bowden, Vivian B. *Faster Than Thought*. Pitman and Sons, 1953.

Campbell-Kelly, Martin. *ICL: A Business and Technical History*. Oxford University Press, 1990.

Flamm, Kenneth. *Creating the Computer*. Brookings Institution, Washington DC, 1988.

Fleck, Glen. *A Computer Perspective*. Harvard University Press, Cambridge, Massachusetts, 1973.

Goldstine, Herman H. *The Computer from Pascal to Von Neumann*. Princeton University Press, Princeton, 1972.

Hodges, Andrew. *Alan Turing: The Enigma of Intelligence*. Burnett Books and Hutchinson Publishing Group, 1983.

Hyman, Anthony. *Charles Babbage: Pioneer of the Computer*. Oxford University Press, 1982.

Lavington, Simon. *Early British Computers: The Story of Vintage Computers and the People Who Built Them*. Manchester University Press, 1980.

Lindgren, Michael. *Glory and Failure: The Difference Engines of Johann Muller, Charles Babbage and Edvard Scheutz*. Linkoping University, Linkoping, 1987.

Metropolis, Nick; Howlett, Jack; and Rota, Gian Carlo (editors). *A History of Computing in the Twentieth Century*. Academic Press, New York, 1980.

Rodgers, William. *Think: A Biography of the Watsons and IBM*. Weidenfeld and Nicholson, 1970.
Wilkes, Maurice V. *Memoirs of a Computer Pioneer*. Massachusetts Institute of Technology Press, Cambridge, Massachusetts, 1985.
Williams, Michael R. *A History of Computing Technology*. Prentice-Hall, 1985.

PLACES TO VISIT

Intending visitors are advised to find out the opening times before making a special journey.

GREAT BRITAIN
Museum of Science and Industry, Liverpool Road Station, Liverpool Road, Castlefield, Manchester M3 4JP. Telephone: 061-832 2244.
National Archive for the History of Computing, Centre for the History of Science, Technology and Medicine, Manchester University, Manchester M13 9PL. Telephone: 061-275 5845.
Science Museum, Exhibition Road, South Kensington, London SW7 2DD. Telephone: 071-938 8000. The largest collection of calculating machines and computers in the UK, which now includes the ICL Historical Collection and is home to the Computer Conservation Society.
Totnes Museum, 70 Fore Street, Totnes, Devon TQ9 5RU. Telephone: 0803 863821 or 862147. Display commemorating the early life of Charles Babbage, which was spent with his family in Totnes.
Whipple Museum of the History of Science, Free School Lane, Cambridge CB2 3RH. Telephone: 0223 334540. Contains, *inter alia,* the Francis Hookham Collection of hand-held calculators.

GERMANY
Deutsches Museum, Museumsinsel 1, 8000 Munich 22, Bavaria.

UNITED STATES OF AMERICA
Charles Babbage Institute, 103 Walter Library, University of Minnesota, Minneapolis, Minnesota 55455. The leading American archival and research centre for the history of computing.
The Boston Computer Museum, Museum Wharf, 300 Congress Street, Boston, Massachusetts 02210.
National Museum of American History, Smithsonian Institution, Washington, DC 20560.